6	7	8	9	10	11	12
13	14	15	16	17	18	19
20	21	22	23	24	25	26
27	28	29	30			

4	5	6	7	8	9	10
11	12	13	14	15	16	17
18	19	20	21	22	23	24
25	26	27	28	29	30	31

BrownTrout Publishers, Inc.
Connecting People to Their Passions

Photography ©2022 Daniel Borris
yogadogz.com

- browntrout.com
- facebook.com/browntroutpublishers
- pinterest.com/browntroutpub
- @browntroutpub

- facebook.com/yogadogz
- @yogadogs
- @yogadogz
- @yogacats_official

SA—World Headquarters
01 Continental Blvd., Suite 200
Segundo, CA 90245 USA
10 607 9010 | Toll Free 800 777 7812
ales@browntrout.com

Canada Toll Free 1 888 254 5842 | sales@browntrout.ca
Australia and New Zealand enquiries@browntrout.com.au
Australia Toll Free 1 800 111 882
New Zealand Toll Free 0 800 888 112

Please Recycle

Yago

Chair Pose

UTKATASANA

✦ Strengthens the ankles, thighs, calves, and spine
✦ Stretches the shoulders and chest
✦ Stimulates the abdominal organs, diaphragm, and heart
✦ Reduces flat feet

January

JANVIER | ENERO

SUNDAY dim • dom	MONDAY lun • lun	TUESDAY mar • mar	WEDNESDAY mer • miér	THURSDAY jeu • jue	FRIDAY ven • vier	SATURDAY sam • sáb
1	2	3	4	5 Full Moon 23:08 UT ○	6	7
New Year's Day	New Year's Day observed (AU; NZ; UK)	Day after New Year's Day observed (NZ; SCT)			Epiphany Día de los Reyes (MX)	
8	9	10	11	12	13	14
15 Last Quarter 2:10 UT ◑	16	17	18	19	20 New Moon 20:53 UT ●	21
	Martin Luther King Jr. Day (US)					
22	23	24	25	26	27	28 First Quarter 15:19 UT ◑
Chinese New Year (Rabbit)			Burns Night (SCT)	Australia Day (AU)	Int'l Holocaust Remembrance Day (UN)	
29	30	31	1	2		

DECEMBER 2022

S	M	T	W	T	F	S
				1	2	3
4	5	6	7	8	9	10
11	12	13	14	15	16	17
18	19	20	21	22	23	24
25	26	27	28	29	30	31

FEBRUARY 2023

S	M	T	W	T	F	S
			1	2	3	4
5	6	7	8	9	10	11
12	13	14	15	16	17	18
19	20	21	22	23	24	25
26	27	28				

2023

YOGA PUPPIES

Bella

Lotus Pose

PADMASANA

▸ Calms the brain
▸ Stimulates the pelvis, spine, and abdomen
▸ Stretches the knees, ankles, and hips

February

FÉVRIER | FEBRERO

SUNDAY dim • dom	MONDAY lun • lun	TUESDAY mar • mar	WEDNESDAY mer • miér	THURSDAY jeu • jue	FRIDAY ven • vier	SATURDAY sam • sáb
29	30	31	1	2 Groundhog Day (US; CAN) Día de la Candelaria (MX)	3	4
Full Moon 18:28 UT ○ 5 Día de la Constitución (MX)	6 Waitangi Day (NZ)	7	8	9	10	11
12 Lincoln's Birthday (US)	Last Quarter 16:01 UT ◑ 13	14 Valentine's Day	15	16	17	18
19	New Moon 7:06 UT ● 20 Presidents' Day (US) Provincial Holiday (CAN except NL/QC)	21 Shrove Tuesday Mardi Gras	22 Ash Wednesday Washington's Birthday (US)	23	24 Día de la Bandera (MX)	25
First Quarter 8:05 UT ◑ 26	27 Great Lent begins (Orthodox)	28	1	2		

JANUARY 2023

S	M	T	W	T	F	S
1	2	3	4	5	6	7
8	9	10	11	12	13	14
15	16	17	18	19	20	21
22	23	24	25	26	27	28
29	30	31				

MARCH 2023

S	M	T	W	T	F	S
			1	2	3	4
5	6	7	8	9	10	11
12	13	14	15	16	17	18
19	20	21	22	23	24	25
26	27	28	29	30	31	

2023

YOGA PUPPI

Lia

Scorpion Pose Variation
VRSCHIKASANA

✦ Stretches the front body and opens the heart
✦ Builds deep core strength
✦ Increases strength and stability in the upper body and back
✦ Improves balance and coordination

March
MARS | MARZO

SUNDAY dim • dom	MONDAY lun • lun	TUESDAY mar • mar	WEDNESDAY mer • miér	THURSDAY jeu • jue	FRIDAY ven • vier	SATURDAY sam • sáb

FEBRUARY 2023
S M T W T F S
1 2 3 4
5 6 7 8 9 10 11
12 13 14 15 16 17 18
19 20 21 22 23 24 25
26 27 28

APRIL 2023
S M T W T F S
1
2 3 4 5 6 7 8
9 10 11 12 13 14 15
16 17 18 19 20 21 22
23 24 25 26 27 28 29
30

28

1
Autumn begins (S. Hemisphere)
St. David's Day (WAL)

2

3

4

5

6
Labour Day (WA-AU)
Purim begins at sundown

7
Full Moon
12:40 UT
○

8
Int'l Women's Day

9

10

11

12
Daylight Saving Time begins (US; CAN)

13
Commonwealth Day (UK)
Canberra Day (ACT-AU)
Eight Hours Day (TAS-AU)
Labour Day (VIC-AU)

14
Last Quarter
2:08 UT
◗

15

16

17
St. Patrick's Day

18

19
Mothering Sunday (UK)

20
New Moon
17:23 UT
●
Spring begins (N. Hemisphere)

21
Natalicio de Benito Juárez (MX)

22
Ramadan begins at sundown

23

24

25

26

27

28
First Quarter
2:32 UT
◗

29

30

31

1

2023   YOGA PU

Dalí

Camel Pose Variation

UTKATASANA

- Counteracts the effects of prolonged slouching
- Stretches the abdomen, chest, shoulders, hip flexors, and quadriceps
- Strengthens the back muscles, hamstrings, and glutes

April
AVRIL | ABRIL

SUNDAY dim • dom	MONDAY lun • lun	TUESDAY mar • mar	WEDNESDAY mer • miér	THURSDAY jeu • jue	FRIDAY ven • vier	SATURDAY sam • sáb
MARCH 2023 S M T W T F S 　　　1 2 3 4 5 6 7 8 9 10 11 12 13 14 15 16 17 18 19 20 21 22 23 24 25 26 27 28 29 30 31	**MAY 2023** S M T W T F S 　1 2 3 4 5 6 7 8 9 10 11 12 13 14 15 16 17 18 19 20 21 22 23 24 25 26 27 28 29 30 31	28	29	30	31	1 April Fools' Day
2 Palm Sunday Daylight Saving Time ends (AU except NT/QLD/WA; NZ)	3	4	5 Passover begins at sundown	Full Moon 4:34 UT ○　6 Maundy Thursday	7 Good Friday Bank Holiday (UK)	8 Holy Saturday
9 Easter Sunday	10 Easter Monday Bank Holiday (UK except SCT; IRL)	11	Last Quarter 9:11 UT ◑　12	13	14	15
16 Pascha (Orthodox)	17 Yom HaShoah begins at sundown	18	New Moon 4:12 UT ●　19	20	21 Birthday of Queen Elizabeth II (AU; CAN; NZ; UK) Eid al-Fitr begins at sundown	22 Earth Day
St. George's Day (ENG; NL-CAN) 23	24	25 Anzac Day (AU; NZ)	26 Administrative Professionals Day	First Quarter 21:20 UT ◐　27 Koningsdag (NL)	28 Arbor Day (US)	29
30　Día del Niño (MX)						

YOGA PUPPIES

Buba
Handstand Pose
ADHO MUKHA VRKSASANA

- ◆ Builds strength in the shoulders, back, and abdomen
- ◆ Enhances mood and increases confidence
- ◆ Strengthens the core and balance

May

MAI | MAYO

SUNDAY dim • dom	MONDAY lun • lun	TUESDAY mar • mar	WEDNESDAY mer • miér	THURSDAY jeu • jue	FRIDAY ven • vier	SATURDAY sam • sáb
30	1 May Day | Int'l Workers' Day Bank/Public Holiday (UK; IRL) Día del Trabajo (MX) Labour Day (QLD-AU) Dag van de Arbeid (BE; NL)	2	3	4 Full Moon 17:34 UT ○ National Day of Prayer (US) Dodenherdenking (NL)	5 Cinco de Mayo (US) Batalla de Puebla (MX) Bevrijdingsdag (NL)	6
7 National Pet Week (US)	8 Fête de la Victoire (FR)	9	10 Día de las Madres (MX)	11	12 Last Quarter 14:28 UT ☽	13
14 Mother's Day (US; AU; BE; CAN; NL; NZ)	15 Día del Maestro (MX)	16	17	18 New Moon 15:53 UT ● Ascension	19	20 Armed Forces Day (US)
21	22 Victoria Day/ Fête de la Reine (CAN) Journée nationale des patriotes/ National Patriots' Day (QC-CAN)	23	24	25	26 National Sorry Day (AU)	27 First Quarter 15:22 UT ◐
28 Pentecost (Whitsun)	29 Pentecost Monday Memorial Day (US) Spring Bank Holiday (UK) Reconciliation Day (ACT-AU)	30	31	1		

APRIL 2023

S	M	T	W	T	F	S
						1
2	3	4	5	6	7	8
9	10	11	12	13	14	15
16	17	18	19	20	21	22
23	24	25	26	27	28	29
30						

JUNE 2023

S	M	T	W	T	F	S
				1	2	3
4	5	6	7	8	9	10
11	12	13	14	15	16	17
18	19	20	21	22	23	24
25	26	27	28	29	30	

2023

YOGA PUPPIES

Rosa

Full Boat Pose

PARIPURNA NAVASANA

✦ Strengthens the core, hip flexors, and thighs
✦ Boosts energy and fights fatigue
✦ Improves posture and counteracts the effects of prolonged sitting

June
JUIN | JUNIO

SUNDAY dim · dom	MONDAY lun · lun	TUESDAY mar · mar	WEDNESDAY mer · miér	THURSDAY jeu · jue	FRIDAY ven · vier	SATURDAY sam · sáb
MAY 2023 S M T W T F S 　　1 2 3 4 5 6 7 8 9 10 11 12 13 14 15 16 17 18 19 20 21 22 23 24 25 26 27 28 29 30 31	**JULY 2023** S M T W T F S 　　　　　　1 2 3 4 5 6 7 8 9 10 11 12 13 14 15 16 17 18 19 20 21 22 23 24 25 26 27 28 29 30 31	30	31	1	2	3
Full Moon 3:42 UT ○　　**4** Fête des Mères (FR)	**5** Public Holiday (IRL) Queen's Birthday (NZ) Western Australia Day (WA-AU)	**6**	**7**	**8**	**9**	Last Quarter 19:31 UT ◑　　**10** Queen's Official Birthday (tentative) (UK)
11 Vaderdag/Fête des Pères (BE)	**12** Queen's Birthday (AU except QLD/WA)	**13**	**14** Flag Day (US)	**15**	**16**	**17**
New Moon 4:37 UT ●　　**18** Father's Day (US; CAN; FR; MX; NL; UK)	**19** Juneteenth (US)	**20**	**21** Summer begins (N. Hemisphere) National Indigenous Peoples Day (NT/YT-CAN)	**22**	**23**	**24** Fête nationale du Québec/ National Holiday of Quebec (QC-CAN)
25	First Quarter 7:50 UT ◐　　**26** June Holiday (NL-CAN)	**27**	**28** Eid al-Adha begins at sundown	**29**	**30**	1

Winter begins (S. Hemisphere)

2023

YOGA PUPPIES

Kerrigan

Half Moon Pose

ARDHA CHANDRASANA

✦ Stretches the hamstrings, calves, shoulders, chest, and spine

✦ Improves digestion

✦ Helps relieve stress

✦ Sustains higher dimensions of energy

July

JUILLET | JULIO

SUNDAY dim • dom	MONDAY lun • lun	TUESDAY mar • mar	WEDNESDAY mer • miér	THURSDAY jeu • jue	FRIDAY ven • vier	SATURDAY sam • sáb
JUNE 2023 S M T W T F S · · · · 1 2 3 4 5 6 7 8 9 10 11 12 13 14 15 16 17 18 19 20 21 22 23 24 25 26 27 28 29 30	**AUGUST 2023** S M T W T F S · · 1 2 3 4 5 6 7 8 9 10 11 12 13 14 15 16 17 18 19 20 21 22 23 24 25 26 27 28 29 30 31	27	28	29	30	1 — Canada Day/Fête du Canada (CAN)
2	Full Moon 11:39 UT ○ 3	4 — Independence Day (US)	5	6	7	8
Nunavut Day (NU-CAN) 9	Last Quarter 1:48 UT ◗ 10	11 — Feest van de Vlaamse Gemeenschap (BE)	12 — Bank Holiday (NIR)	13	14 — Fête nationale de la France (FR)	15
16	New Moon 18:32 UT ● 17	18 — Muharram begins at sundown	19	20	21 — Nationale feestdag/ Fête nationale de la Belgique (BE)	22
23	24	First Quarter 22:07 UT ◑ 25	26	27 — Ashura begins at sundown	28	29
30	31					

2023

YOGA PUPPIES

Dustin

Side Crane Pose

PARSVA BAKASANA

✦ Strengthens the shoulders and upper body
✦ Challenges breathing, balance, and flexibility
✦ Tones the belly and spine
✦ Activates the naval chakra

August
AOÛT | AGOSTO

SUNDAY dim • dom	MONDAY lun • lun	TUESDAY mar • mar	WEDNESDAY mer • miér	THURSDAY jeu • jue	FRIDAY ven • vier	SATURDAY sam • sáb
JULY 2023 S M T W T F S 1 2 3 4 5 6 7 8 9 10 11 12 13 14 15 16 17 18 19 20 21 22 23 24 25 26 27 28 29 30 31	**SEPTEMBER 2023** S M T W T F S 1 2 3 4 5 6 7 8 9 10 11 12 13 14 15 16 17 18 19 20 21 22 23 24 25 26 27 28 29 30	Full Moon 18:32 UT ○ **1**	**2**	**3**	**4**	**5**
6	**7** Civic Holiday/Congé civique (CAN except NL/QC/YT) Bank Holiday (IRL; SCT) Picnic Day (NT-AU)	Last Quarter 10:28 UT ◑ **8**	**9**	**10**	**11**	**12**
13	**14**	**15** Assumption	New Moon 9:38 UT ● **16** Royal Queensland Show (QLD-AU)	**17**	**18**	**19**
20	**21** Discovery Day (YT-CAN)	**22**	**23** First Quarter 9:57 UT ◐	**24**	**25**	**26**
27	**28** Summer Bank Holiday (UK except SCT)	**29**	**30**	**31** Full Moon 1:35 UT ○	1	2

YOGA PUPPIES

Cosmo

Side Crow Pose, Extended Leg Variation
PARSVA KAKASANA

✦ Strengthens the wrists, elbows, and arms
✦ Increases hip and spinal flexibility
✦ Massages the abdominal organs
✦ Intensifies core strength

September

SEPTEMBRE | SEPTIEMBRE **NATIONAL YOGA MONTH**

SUNDAY dim • dom	MONDAY lun • lun	TUESDAY mar • mar	WEDNESDAY mer • miér	THURSDAY jeu • jue	FRIDAY ven • vier	SATURDAY sam • sáb
AUGUST 2023 S M T W T F S 1 2 3 4 5 6 7 8 9 10 11 12 13 14 15 16 17 18 19 20 21 22 23 24 25 26 27 28 29 30 31	**OCTOBER 2023** S M T W T F S 1 2 3 4 5 6 7 8 9 10 11 12 13 14 15 16 17 18 19 20 21 22 23 24 25 26 27 28 29 30 31	29	30	31	1 Spring begins (S. Hemisphere)	2
3 Father's Day (AU; NZ)	4 Labor Day (US) Labour Day/Fête du travail (CAN)	5 Last Quarter 22:21 UT	6	7	8	9
10 National Grandparents Day (US)	11 Patriot Day/National Day of Service and Remembrance (US)	12	13	14 New Moon 1:40 UT	15 Noche del Grito (MX) Rosh Hashanah begins at sundown	16 Día de la Independencia (MX)
17 Australian Citizenship Day (AU)	18	19	20	21 UN Int'l Day of Peace	22 First Quarter 19:32 UT	23 Autumn begins (N. Hemisphere)
24 Daylight Saving Time begins (NZ) Yom Kippur begins at sundown	25 Queen's Birthday (WA–AU)	26	27 Fête de la Communauté Française (BE)	28 Full Moon 9:57 UT	29	30

2023

YOGA PUPPIES

Giselle

Balancing Table Pose

DANDAYAMNA BHARMANASANA

✦ Improves spinal flexibility and abdominal strength
✦ Stretches the back, torso, and neck
✦ Develops postural awareness and balance
✦ Brings the spine into alignment

October
OCTOBRE | OCTUBRE

SUNDAY dim • dom	MONDAY lun • lun	TUESDAY mar • mar	WEDNESDAY mer • miér	THURSDAY jeu • jue	FRIDAY ven • vier	SATURDAY sam • sáb
1	2	3	4	5	6	7
Daylight Saving Time begins (AU except NT/QLD/WA)	Labour Day (ACT/NSW/SA-AU) Queen's Birthday (QLD-AU)		World Animal Day		Last Quarter 13:48 UT	
8	9	10	11	12	13	14
	Indigenous Peoples' Day/ Columbus Day (US) Thanksgiving Day/ Action de grâce (CAN)			Día de la Raza (MX)	New Moon 17:55 UT	
15	16	17	18	19	20	21
	Boss's Day					
22	23	24	25	26	27	28
First Quarter 3:29 UT	Labour Day (NZ)	United Nations Day			Full Moon 20:24 UT	
29	30	31	1	2		
	Public Holiday (IRL)	Halloween				

SEPTEMBER 2023

S	M	T	W	T	F	S
					1	2
3	4	5	6	7	8	9
10	11	12	13	14	15	16
17	18	19	20	21	22	23
24	25	26	27	28	29	30

NOVEMBER 2023

S	M	T	W	T	F	S
			1	2	3	4
5	6	7	8	9	10	11
12	13	14	15	16	17	18
19	20	21	22	23	24	25
26	27	28	29	30		

2023

YOGA PUPPIES

Flower

One-Armed Handstand Pose

**EKA HASTA ADHO
MUKHA VRKSASANA**

✦ Improves posture
✦ Reduces swelling in
the ankles and feet
✦ Boosts energy and
fights fatigue
✦ Strengthens all the
major muscles